Whoosh!

'Whoosh!'
An original concept by Katie Dale
© Katie Dale

Illustrated by Letizia Rizzo

Published by MAVERICK ARTS PUBLISHING LTD
Studio 11, City Business Centre, 6 Brighton Road,
Horsham, West Sussex, RH13 5BB
© Maverick Arts Publishing Limited August 2020
+44 (0)1403 256941

A CIP catalogue record for this book is available at the British Library.

ISBN 978-1-84886-687-4

Maverick
publishing
www.maverickbooks.co.uk

Green

This book is rated as: Green Band (Guided Reading)
This story is mostly decodable at Letters and Sounds Phase 5.
Up to five non-decodable story words are included.

Whoosh!

by Katie Dale

illustrated by
Letizia Rizzo

Ben looked out of the window.

Dad's car was coming
down the road. Hooray!

"We're going to have a GREAT day, Dad!" Ben cried. "Let's go to the park!"

But just as they got to the park...

WHOOSH!

The wind blew Dad's hat off!

"Oh no!" cried Ben. He ran after it,
but it flew away.

"Never mind," said Dad.

"Let's have a picnic!"

But just as they got out
a packet of crisps...

WHOOSH!

The wind blew the crisp packet away!
"Oh no!" cried Ben. He ran after the
crisps, but they blew away.

"Never mind," said Dad.

"Let's feed the ducks."

But just as they got to the pond...

WHOOSH!

The wind blew the seeds away!

"Oh no!" cried Ben.

"Never mind," said Dad.

"Let's play ball."

But just as Ben kicked the ball...

WHOOSH!

The wind blew the ball into

a tall tree! It was stuck!

"Oh no!" cried Ben.

"Never mind," said Dad.

"Let's go home."

Ben was sad.

He went up to his room.

"What's the matter?" Dad asked.

"We could not have a picnic or feed the ducks or play ball," Ben said sadly. "The wind has spoiled our day!"

Dad gave Ben a hug.

"The day is not over yet,"

said Dad, smiling.

"And a windy day is GREAT for...

...flying a kite!"

Ben and Dad went to a big hill.

WHOOSH!

The wind blew leaves all around them. It was fun!

Ben and Dad ran up the hill.

WHOOSH!

The wind blew Ben's coat like a cape.

"I feel like a superhero!" Ben cried.

When they got to the top of the hill,
Dad held the string and Ben ran
as fast as he could.

Then suddenly…

WHOOSH!

The kite flew high, high up into the sky!

"We did it!" Ben cried.

Ben smiled.

"This IS a great day after all!" he said.

Dad hugged him tight.

"Yes it is," said Dad.

Quiz

1. Who's car was coming down the road in the beginning?
a) Ben's
b) Dad's
c) Mum's

2. What piece of clothing blows away in the wind?
a) A scarf
b) A hat
c) A sock

3. Why can't Ben and Dad feed the ducks?
a) They have the wrong food
b) There are no ducks
c) The wind blew the seeds away

4. What does Dad get out of his car?

a) A new scarf

b) A kite

c) A ball

5. "This IS a _____ day after all!" said Ben.

a) Great

b) Bad

c) Fun

Turn over for answers

Book Bands for Guided Reading

The Institute of Education book banding system is a scale of colours that reflects the various levels of reading difficulty. The bands are assigned by taking into account the content, the language style, the layout and phonics. Word, phrase and sentence level work is also taken into consideration.

Maverick Early Readers are a bright, attractive range of books covering the pink to white bands. All of these books have been book banded for guided reading to the industry standard and edited by a leading educational consultant.

To view the whole Maverick Readers scheme, visit our website at
www.maverickearlyreaders.com

Or scan the QR code above to view our scheme instantly!

Quiz Answers: 1b, 2b, 3c, 4b, 5a